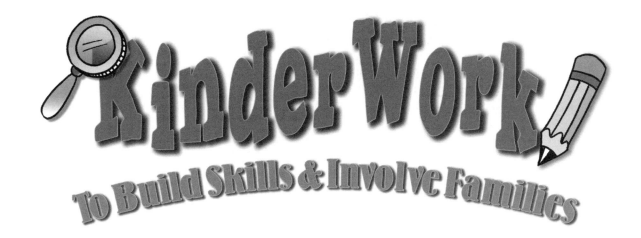

KinderWork!
To Build Skills & Involve Families

by Keri King & Kari Sickman

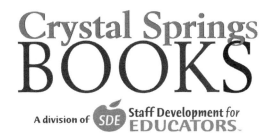

Crystal Springs
BOOKS

A division of SDE Staff Development for EDUCATORS

Peterborough, New Hampshire

Published by Crystal Springs Books
A division of Staff Development for Educators (SDE)
10 Sharon Road, PO Box 500
Peterborough, NH 03458
1-800-321-0401
www.crystalsprings.com
www.sde.com

© 2005 Keri King and Kari Sickman
Illustrations © 2005 Crystal Springs Books

Published 2005
Printed in the United States of America
09 08 07 06   2 3 4 5
ISBN-13: 978-1-884548-85-7
ISBN-10: 1-884548-85-7

Editor: Sharon Smith
Art Director, Designer, and Production Coordinator: Soosen Dunholter
Illustrator: Marci McAdam

To our students.

Contents

Introduction

Reinforcement is an important part of retaining skills. Home practice can be an excellent means of reinforcement, but it's often a challenge for teachers to come up with take-home activity sheets that motivate students, involve families, and reinforce skills effectively. *KinderWork* is intended to do exactly those things.

KinderWork is a resource book that has been designed to integrate reading, writing, and math into one fun and easy-to-use book for kindergarten students and their families. We have started with a common part of the kindergarten curriculum, the alphabet, and created math, reading, and writing activities to support this focus and at the same time involve parents.

KinderWork reviews many of the skills being taught in kindergarten classrooms today to help young students meet state and federal standards. (You can quickly identify which activities address which math skills by checking the chart on page 10.) The activities can be completed in or out of alphabetical order, depending on your needs and those of your students. Either way, by completing these sheets over the course of the school year, each student has a chance to practice skills and to create her own unique alphabet book.

You may wish to utilize the activity sheets included here for classroom lessons. However, we believe the greatest strength of these activities is in their potential for building the connection between home and school.

KinderWork offers a repetitive format and simple directions that make the activity sheets easy for teachers, students, and families to use. By sending the activity sheets home either individually or bound together in a book, you can involve parents in their children's learning and familiarize them with what's going on at school.

We've found that preassembling the books, in whatever order meets your students' needs, can be helpful for keeping the activity sheets moving between home and school. We have included a cover for the book and a sample letter to parents/guardians; you can include both in the front of the bound book for easy reference or send them home with the first of the individual activity sheets.

If some of your students' parents are involved only to a limited degree, you may wish to seek the assistance of a parent volunteer or paraprofessional to work with those children in completing the assignments. Expectations for each student may also vary, depending upon family situations and student abilities.

Students come with different levels of knowledge and abilities. *KinderWork* has been designed to meet these varied levels with basic letter practice and more advanced reading and writing activities. The math skills addressed cover a wide range of abilities as well. However, your options don't stop there. If you wish to differentiate activities further, consider the following possibilities.

To Reinforce Reading and Writing Skills
- Have the child make a list of words that start with the letter being studied or cut appropriate words and/or pictures from newspapers and magazines.
- Ask the child to write a story about the object associated with the letter in the activity sheet. (For example, have the child write about the apple tree pictured in the activities for the letter *a*.)
- For each sight word, have the child write a sentence that includes that word.

To Reinforce Math Skills
- Extend each math activity by using bigger or different numbers.
- Create your own math problems (have the child make her own pattern, story problem, or graph).

However you choose to use *KinderWork,* you will enjoy watching your students get excited about learning, take responsibility and pride in their work, and build their academic skills.

Math Skills Addressed with Each Letter

	Addition	Counting	Estimation	Graphs	Measurement	Money	Number Recognition	Number Sense	Number Writing	Patterns	Problem Solving	Shapes	Subtraction	Symmetry	Tally Marks
A	X	X					X		X						
B										X					
C												X			
D		X					X		X						
E		X					X	X	X						
F		X		X			X								
G							X	X							
H		X					X	X	X						
I														X	
J		X	X			X	X		X		X				
K		X					X	X	X						
L										X					
M						X	X		X						
N		X					X	X	X						
O	X	X					X	X	X						
P		X				X	X		X						
Q		X					X								X
R	X	X					X		X		X				
S		X					X	X	X						
T		X					X	X	X				X		
U		X					X	X	X						
V										X					
W							X		X						
X													X		
Y					X		X	X							
Z	X	X					X		X		X				

Dear Parent or Guardian,

As you know, practice is one of the best ways to reinforce the new skills students are learning at school. This year your child will be asked to complete certain activities at home and then bring the completed work back to school. Your child will need a pencil, crayons, scissors, glue, old magazines—and your guidance.

All of the activities are based on learning the alphabet, and they all follow the same basic format. Here are step-by-step directions for your child to follow.

Side One

1. Handwriting
Trace each letter and then print three uppercase and three lowercase letters, using a pencil and a top-to-bottom motion.

2. Picture
Follow the directions.
Draw or use magazine pictures to complete the activity.

3. Math
Complete the math activity.

Side Two

1. Letter and Word Find
Read the sentences with a grown-up.
Circle the letters and underline the words.

2. Read and Write
Reread each sentence.
Complete the last sentence by filling in the blank.

3. Writing Words
Trace each word and then write it two times, using a pencil and a top-to-bottom motion.

Be creative, do your best work, and—most important—have fun!

Sincerely,

My Alphabet Book

_____

A a

Draw 3 <u>red</u> apples on the tree.

Draw 2 <u>yellow</u> apples on the tree.

Draw 1 <u>green</u> apple on the tree.

How many apples are on the tree? _____

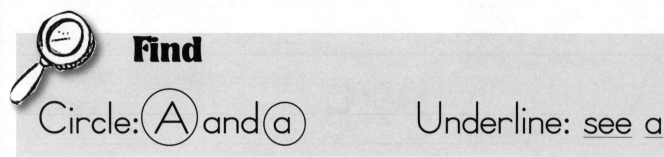

Apples

I see a red apple.

I see a yellow apple.

I see a green apple.

I see a _____ apple.

 **Trace each word and then write it two times.**

see _____ _____

a _____ _____

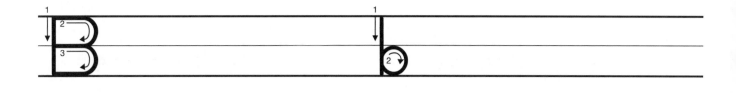

Add 2 objects to the box. Each object should start with the letter Bb.

Use two colors to color the bears and make an AB pattern.

A   B   A   B   A   B

Bears

Bears like honey.

Bears like berries.

Bears like fish.

I like _____.

Trace each word and then write it two times.

like _____ _____

I _____ _____

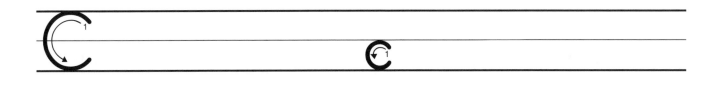

Color the ◯ yellow.   Color the ☐s orange.

Color the △s red.   Color the ▭s blue.

Color the ⬭ brown.   Color the ◇s black.

Cats

Cats like to play.

Cats like to sleep.

Cats like to climb.

I like to _____.

Trace each word and then write it two times.

to   _____ _____

like   _____ _____

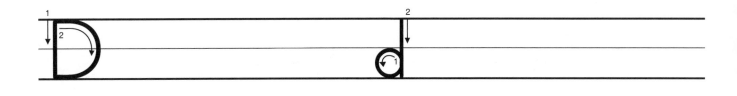

Add one object to the dinosaur's back. The object should start with the letter Dd.

Count the dots on the dominoes and write those numbers.

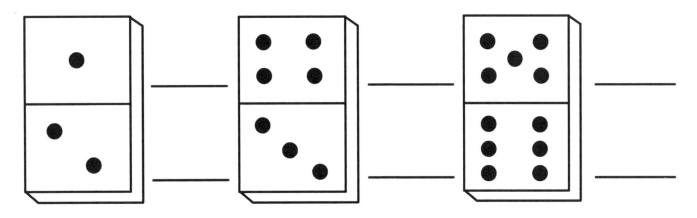

Find

Circle: D and d   Underline: the   see

Dinosaurs

I see the big dinosaur.

I see the small dinosaur.

I see the green dinosaur.

I see the _____ dinosaur.

Trace each word and then write it two times.

the _____ _____

see _____ _____

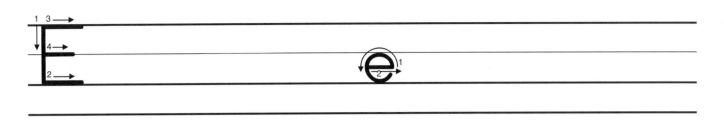

Elephant is sending you a letter. Write your name and address on the envelope.

Write the missing numbers on the eggs.

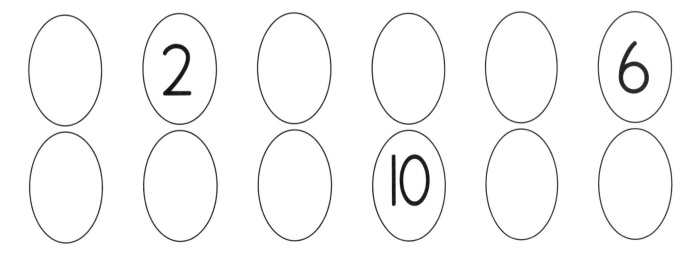

Find

The Elephant

The elephant is big.
The elephant is gray.
The elephant is eating

_____ .

 **Trace each word and then write it two times.**

is _____ _____

the _____ _____

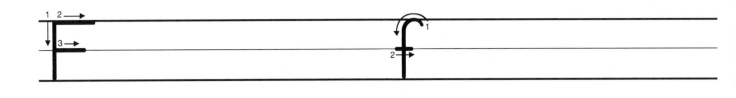

Graph the fish in the picture.

4				
3				
2				
1				

My Fish

My fish is my pet.

My fish is orange.

My fish is small.

My fish is _____.

Trace each word and then write it two times.

my _____ _____

is _____ _____

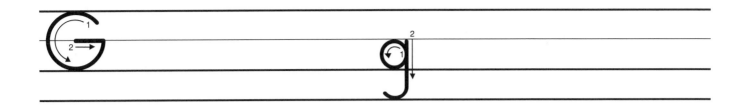

Add grass and two other objects that start with the letter Gg.

Color the largest number in each bunch of grapes.

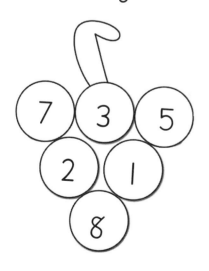
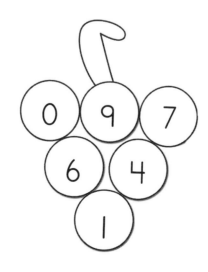
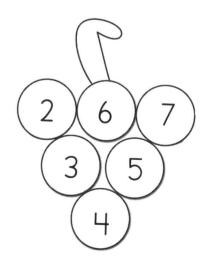

My Goat

My goat can eat.

My goat can run.

My goat can play.

My goat can _____.

Trace each word and then write it two times.

can _____ _____

my _____ _____

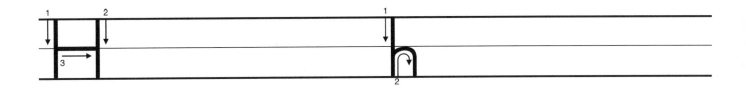

Add two objects in front of the horse. Each object should start with the letter Hh.

Write the numbers between 0 and 20 in the hearts.

The Horse

The horse can go to the barn.

The horse can go to my house.

The horse can go to sleep.

The horse can go _____.

Trace each word and then write it two times.

go   _____   _____

can   _____   _____

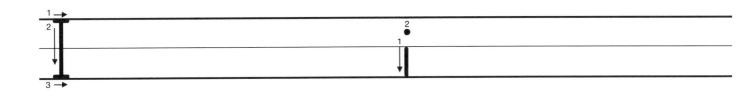

Draw an insect on the flower.

Draw the other half of each insect.

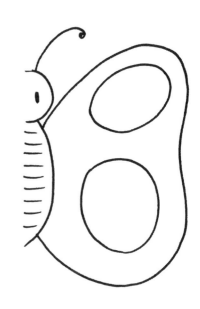

Insects

Insects can crawl and fly.

Insects can bite and sting.

Insects can lay eggs.

I can _____ and _____.

Trace each word and then write it two times.

and _____ _____

can _____ _____

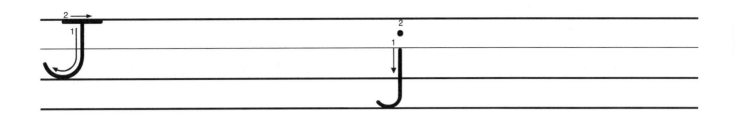

Add two objects to the jack-in-the-box. Each object should start with the letter Jj.

Estimate how many pennies you think will fit on the jar. Write your estimate in the Estimation box. Now lay down real pennies to find out! In the Actual box, write the number of pennies that fit on the jar.

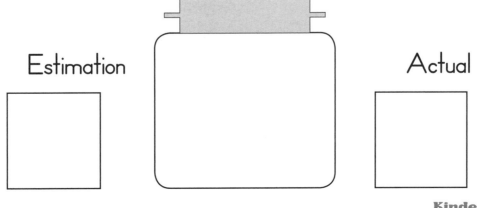

Estimation

Actual

Jack-in-the-Box

My jack-in-the-box is blue.

My jack-in-the-box is a toy.

My jack-in-the-box is in

_____.

Trace each word and then write it two times.

in _____ _____

is _____ _____

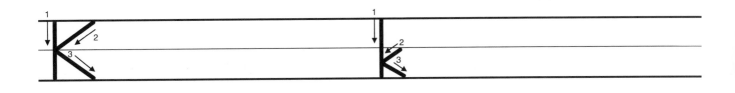

Add two objects that the king will put in his castle. Each object should start with the letter Kk.

Count backward. Write in the missing numbers.

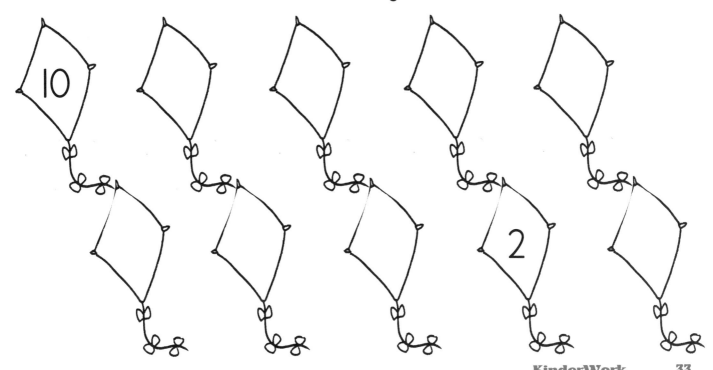

The King

The king is kind.

He wears a crown and a cape.

He has a kitten and a

_____.

Trace each word and then write it two times.

he _____   _____

and _____   _____

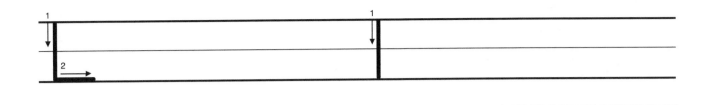

Add two objects that the lion likes to eat. Each object should start with the letter Ll.

Use three colors to color the lollipops and make an ABC pattern.

A   B   C   A   B   C   A   B   C

The Lion

Look, the lion is in the cage.

Look, the lion is eating.

Look, the lion is roaring.

Look, the lion can _____.

Trace each word and then write it two times.

look _____ _____

the _____ _____

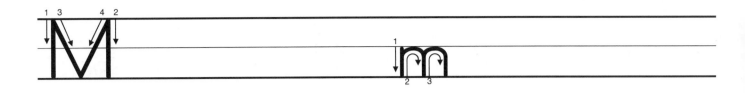

Add two objects that the moose will buy with money. Both objects should start with the letter Mm.

Write the value of each coin in the box next to the coin.

Circle: (M) and (m)   Underline: <u>at</u> <u>look</u>

The Moose

Look at the moose!

He is big and brown.

Look, the moose is at the

_____.

Trace each word and then write it two times.

at _____ _____

look _____ _____

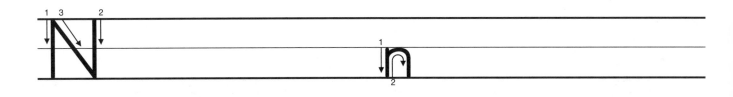

Add two objects to the nurse's clipboard. Each object should start with the letter Nn.

Write the missing numbers in the nuts.

The Nurse

You can see the nurse.

The nurse can help you.

She can _____.

Trace each word and then write it two times.

you _____ _____

can _____ _____

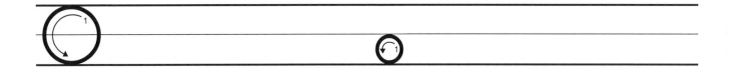

Add two objects that the octopus sees in the ocean.

On each olive, write the number that is one more.

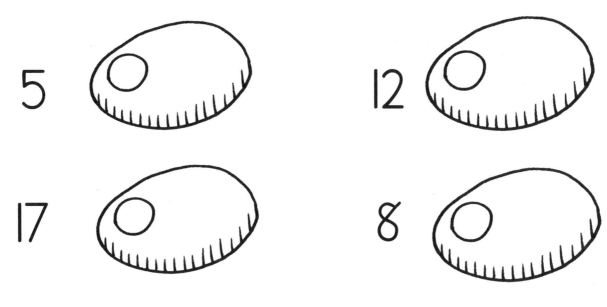

5

12

17

8

The Octopus

The octopus is on a rock.

The octopus is on a ship.

The octopus is on _____.

Trace each word and then write it two times.

on _____ _____

is _____ _____

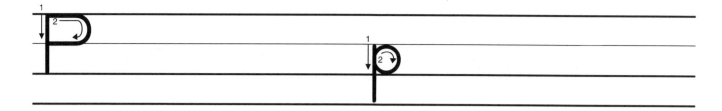

Add two objects in the mud. Each object should start with the letter Pp.

Count the money in each piggy bank. Write the total on the line.

Circle: Ⓟ and ⓟ   Underline: <u>do</u> <u>you</u>

The Pig

Do you see the pink pig?

Do you see the pig in the mud?

Do you see the pig in the

_____?

Trace each word and then write it two times.

do _____ _____

you _____ _____

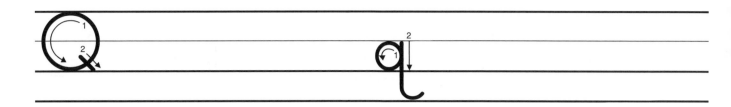

Q q

Add two objects that the queen will use in her castle. Each object should start with the letter Qq.

Flip a quarter 10 times. Tally the number of heads and tails.

heads

tails

The Queen

The queen is pretty.

She is nice.

The queen is happy.

She is _____.

 **Trace each word and then write it two times.**

she _____ _____

is _____ _____

Tom

Kim

Tom has 2 orange carrots. Kim has 5 orange carrots. How many carrots do they have in all? Draw the carrots in the boxes. Write the numbers on the lines.

_____ + _____ = _____

Find

The Rabbit

We can hop like a rabbit.

We can eat like a rabbit.

We can run like a rabbit.

We can _____.

Trace each word and then write it two times.

we _____ _____

can _____ _____

S   s

Add sand and two other objects that start with the letter Ss.

Write the numbers that come before and after.

The Snake

Go get the snake!
The snake will go get the mouse.
The snake will go get

_____.

Trace each word and then write it two times.

get   _____ _____

go   _____ _____

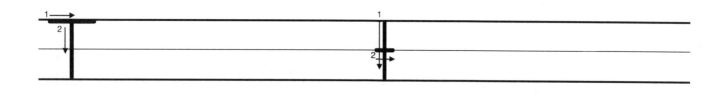

Add two objects that are good for the tiger's teeth.

On each tooth, write the number that is one less.

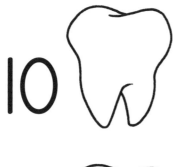

10

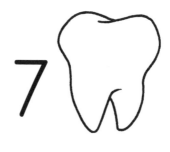

7

3

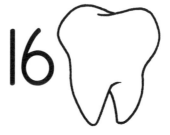

16

Tigers

Tigers are cats.

Tigers are orange and black.

Tigers are at the zoo.

Tigers are _____.

Trace each word and then write it two times.

are _____ _____

at _____ _____

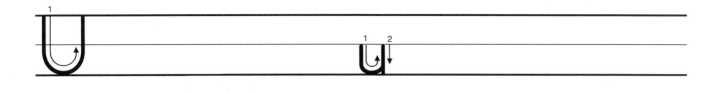

Add two objects under the umbrella. Each object should start with the letter Uu.

Count by 2s. Write the missing numbers in the raindrops.

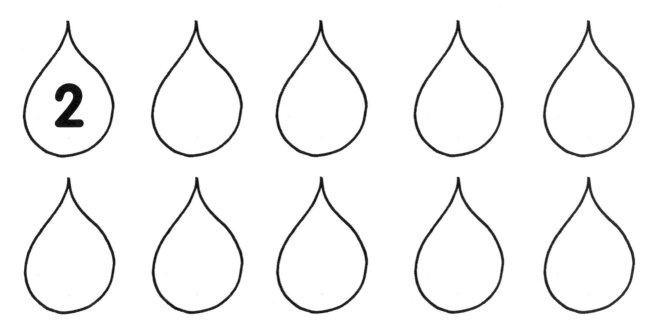

Find

Circle: U and u   Underline: it is

The Umbrella

It is raining.

Can you get my umbrella?

It is big and blue.

The umbrella is _____.

Trace each word and then write it two times.

it _____ _____

is _____ _____

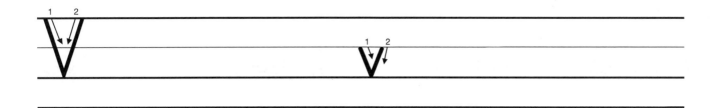

Mouse is wearing his valentine vest! Make a valentine for Mouse.

Use two colors to color the valentines and make an ABB pattern.

A   B   B   A   B   B   A   B   B

Circle: Ⓥ and ⓥ   Underline: <u>here</u> <u>are</u>

My Vest

Here is my vest.

Here are the buttons.

Here are the pockets.

The vest is _____.

Trace each word and then write it two times.

here _____ _____

are _____ _____

What is worm watching? Add two objects. Each object should start with the letter Ww.

Read the number word on each wagon and write that number in the box.

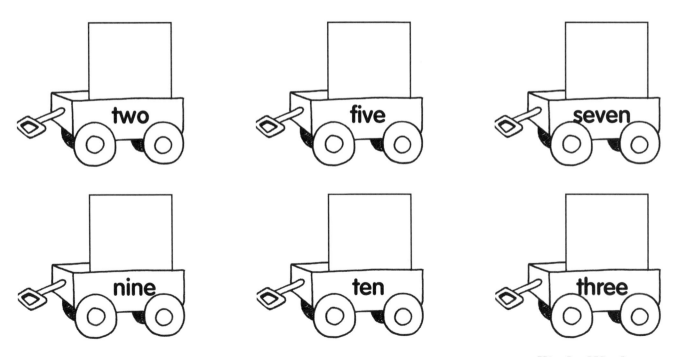

Worms

It is raining.

Here come the worms.

Come and look at the worms.

The worms are _____.

 **Trace each word and then write it two times.**

come _____ _____

the _____ _____

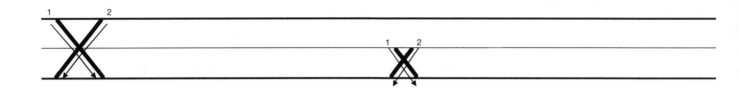

Here is an X-ray. Draw what is inside.

Play a game of tic-tac-toe with a partner.

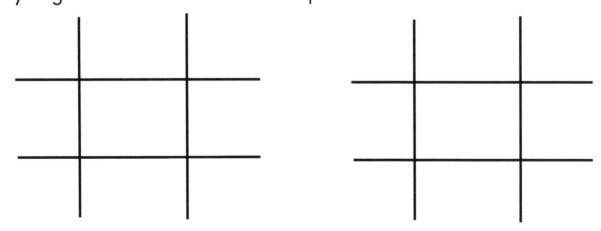

Find

Circle: Ⓧ and ⓧ   Underline: <u>this</u> <u>my</u>

X-ray

This is an X-ray of my arm.

This is an X-ray of my leg.

This is an X-ray of my

_____.

Trace each word and then write it two times.

this _____ _____

my _____ _____

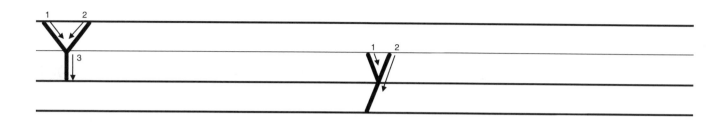

Color the objects that are made out of yarn.

This yarn is _____ inches long.

|||||||||||||||||||||||||||||||||||||||||||||||||||||||||||||||||||||||||||||||||

| | 1 | | 2 | | 3 | | 4 | | 5 | | 6 | | 7 |

This yarn is _____ inches long.

|||||||||||||||||||||||||||||||||||||||||||||||||||||||||||||||

| | 1 | | 2 | | 3 | | 4 | | 5 | | 6 | | 7 |

Yarn

I have yellow yarn.

Do you have yellow mittens?

I have a yellow scarf.

Do you have yellow_____?

Trace each word and then write it two times.

have _____ _____

you _____ _____

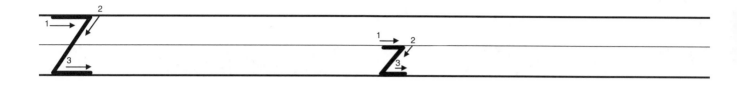

Bob

Pam

Bob sees 2 zebras at the zoo. Pam sees 3 zebras at the zoo. How many zebras do they see in all? Draw the zebras in the boxes. Write the numbers on the lines.

The Zebra

The zebra is in the zoo.

It has black stripes.

It has white stripes.

The zebra has _____.

Trace each word and then write it two times.

has _____ _____

the _____ _____